# BEAU PEEP

## BOOK 19

Published By

**Pedigree**®
BOOKS

Pedigree Books Limited, The Old Rectory, Matford Lane, Exeter, Devon EX2 4PS.

ISBN 1.874507.68.6
Printed in Italy.

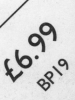

£6.99
BP19

BEAU PEEP

EGON

THE NOMAD

MAD PIERRE

DENNIS

HAMISH

SERGEANT BIDET

COLONEL ESCARGOT

THE VULTURE

A photo of Roger Kettle (writer) and Andrew Christine (artist) taken shortly before Kettle leaned forward to tie his shoe-lace and Christine crashed sideways to the floor.

# THE ADVENTURES OF LEGIONNAIRE
# BEAU PEEP

Peep at Christmas

THUR 5604

I'M GIVING YOU PLENTY OF ADVANCE WARNING, DAD.

I'VE DECIDED TO SPEND CHRISTMAS WITH ALISON AND IAN.

BUT THEY'RE... THEY'RE...

YES, DAD— THEY'RE ROBINS.

FRI 5605

SO YOU'RE GOING TO SPEND CHRISTMAS WITH A COUPLE OF ROBINS?

IT'S BECAUSE THEY'RE FUN, DAD — THEY PLAY GAMES LIKE CHARADES!

SEE IF IT'S STILL FUN WHEN THEY'VE MIMED "GOES BOB-BOB-BOBBIN' ALONG" FOR THE 1,000th TIME.

SAT 5606

YOU'RE SO NARROW-MINDED, DAD.

YOU SHOULD MINGLE MORE — YOU COULD LEARN A LOT FROM OTHER SPECIES OF BIRDS!

WELL, COCK-A-DOODLE DO.

Chapter Two:—
Where to take a girl on your first date.

THUR 5717

It is important to select somewhere interesting which will stimulate conversation.

How about a Sheep-shearing Contest?

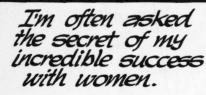

I'm often asked the secret of my incredible success with women.

FRI: 5718

I think honesty is the key.

Avoid that and you're laughing.

Dear Publishers, I enclose my guidebook on how to get a girlfriend.

SAT 5719

It's aimed at helping sensitive men overcome their shyness with the opposite sex.

See, particularly, Chapter 4—"Eat tonsils, Megababe!"

SERGEANTS' EXAM.

QUESTION ONE:—

NAME THE THREE COMPONENTS OF A STANDARD ISSUE RIFLE.

Bottom bit, middle bit and pointy bit.

THUR 5777

SERGEANTS' EXAM.

QUESTION 11:—

FRI 5778

ON A COMPASS, WHAT IS DIRECTLY OPPOSITE NORTH NORTH EAST?

I think you've made a mistake here—you've written "NORTH" twice.

SERGEANTS' EXAM.

YOUR PATROL IS SURROUNDED BY THE ENEMY.

SAT 5779

ALTHOUGH OUTNUMBERED YOUR TOP MARKSMEN ARE IN GOOD POSITION TO ATTACK. WHAT IS YOUR DECISION?

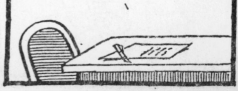

To go for a pint and remain a private—

| | | |
|---|---|---|
| Doctor McHunk began the brain operation.  | It was tricky and dangerous but he remained cool.  | "Hold my cigar, nurse," he said.  |
| THUR: 5783 | | |
| The brain operation was proving to be very tough.  | Doctor McHunk held out his hand. "Scalpel" he said, Forceps...  | "...Crow-bar." |
| FRI: 5784 | | |
| DEAR SIR, THANK YOU FOR SENDING US YOUR LATEST NOVEL.  | IT'S BRILLIANT! WE WANT TO PUBLISH IT! WE'LL GIVE YOU A MILLION POUNDS!  | ONLY JOKING— IT'S AS BIG A PILE OF GARBAGE AS EVERYTHING ELSE YOU'VE SENT! |
| SAT: 5785 | | |

THOSE VULTURES ARE OUT THERE AGAIN.

MON: 5864

I HATE THE WAY THEY SWAY FROM SIDE TO SIDE — IT'S LIKE SOME HORRIBLE DANCE OF DEATH.

OH, HAPPY DAYS ARE HERE AGAIN

I'VE GOT A NEW GIRLFRIEND, DAD.

TUES: 5865

THAT'S GREAT, SON! WHAT'S HER NAME?

I'M NOT SURE...

...I DON'T SPEAK PELICAN TOO WELL.

HOW DID YOU MEET THIS PELICAN GIRLFRIEND OF YOURS, SON?

WED: 5866

THEY'RE WATER-BIRDS —THERE'S NO WATER ROUND HERE.

SHE WAS LOST.

OH, GREAT—MY SON'S DATING A DISORIENTATED PELICAN!

THUR: 5867

I CAN'T BELIEVE YOU'RE DATING A PELICAN, SON!

THE WHOLE BUSINESS HAS DISASTER WRITTEN ALL OVER IT.

IF SHE HICCUPS WHILE YOU'RE KISSING, YOU COULD BE LOST IN THAT BILL FOR EVER!

FRI: 5868

NORMA MAY BE A PELICAN BUT I LOVE HER!

I KNEW THAT THE MOMENT MY LIPS TOUCHED HERS!

OR RATHER, THE MOMENT MY LIPS TOUCHED THE FISH HANGING OUT OF HER MOUTH.

SAT: 5869

WHAT IS IT WITH YOU, SON?

YOU KEEPING DATING THESE WEIRD BIRDS! A BUDGIE... A DUCK... A PELICAN...

I'M GLAD HE DOESN'T KNOW ABOUT TAMMY, THE TAP-DANCING TURKEY!

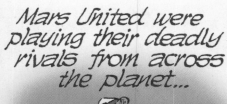

The Martian Cup-final was a tough affair.

THUR 5879

The tackling was ferocious.

Krog, the Mars United winger, got carried off with a broken tentacle.

THIS NEW NOVEL OF MINE IS BRILLIANT! IT'S GOT EVERYTHING!

FRI 5880

DRAMA... INTRIGUE... ROMANCE... ADVENTURE...

...A RECIPE FOR PANCAKES!

A REGISTERED LETTER FROM MY PUBLISHER!

SAT 5881

HE'S NEVER SENT A REGISTERED LETTER BEFORE! IT MUST MEAN HE'S FINALLY ACCEPTED A BOOK OF MINE!

FOOLED YOU! ANOTHER REJECTION!